1968

Merry Xmas
to Ronnie

Geo Anne
and
Peter

1968

The Big Book of Things To Do and Make

By HELEN JILL FLETCHER

Illustrated by INGRID FETZ

RANDOM HOUSE
NEW YORK

Contents

INTRODUCTION

This is a new kind of arts and crafts book for children based on the premise that all young children are imaginative and creative. It's a book of discovering and doing things. Each new discovery is like a key opening the door and encouraging the child to do new things; each new thing done a stimulant to try other things.

All of the projects in this book can be done by very young children. Sometimes a child will require a little help or guidance from an older person. This should be given him just as help is given by a teacher in a classroom.

All of the projects in this book are made from discarded or waste materials plus the simple materials found in most homes where there are young children. None of the projects requires any special materials, tools, or even special talents. Some projects are creative, some are useful, and some are just plain fun. But all have one purpose in common and that is to satisfy the inner urge in a child to create.

You will notice that the book, for the most part, is addressed directly to the child. This is done so that the older person who helps and guides will know how to talk to a child, how to encourage and stimulate him and, most important, how to understand him.

HELEN JILL FLETCHER
(TEACHER IN THE NEW YORK CITY PUBLIC SCHOOLS)

Play with Clay, Soap, and Cork

It is wonderful to play with clay, which is easy to make into shapes and feels good to the touch. When it dries it gets hard so you can save some of the things you make. If you don't like what you make you can make something else of the same clay if you keep it moist. There are different kinds of clay. Some are mixed with water and some are mixed with oil. The kind of clay we're going to use is mixed with water. It's called "moist clay."

Tools and Materials You Will Need

Tools: You don't need regular tools to make wonderful clay objects. Your fingers and hands are the best clay tools. Use them as much as possible. To do what your fingers can't, you can use many things you will find around the house such as orange sticks, meat skewers, lollipop sticks, pencils, hairpins, dull knives, spoons, forks, and a rolling pin.

Other Necessary Materials

Clay: Buy about five pounds from an art supply or department store. Be sure you don't get an oil-base clay.

Oilcloth, Plastic or Newspapers: Spread any one of these over the area where you're going to work.

Wooden Block, Board, or Heavy Cardboard: Use one of these as a base on which to work. Turn the base as you work so that you can see your sculpture from all sides.

Cover Cloth or Plastic: Cover unfinished work with a damp cloth or piece of plastic to keep it moist and soft.

Work Clothes: Wear a smock, apron, or father's old shirt buttoned down the back to protect your clothes.

Painting and Preserving Clay

Painting Clay: Use thick tempera, poster, or house paint on objects that are dry and hard. If you want to use more than one color, let one color dry before applying the next.
Preserving Clay: Liquid wax, shellac, clear varnish (from hardware and paint supply stores) and colorless nail polish can be applied to clay objects after they are dry. This will prevent the paint from rubbing off and will give the object a high gloss.

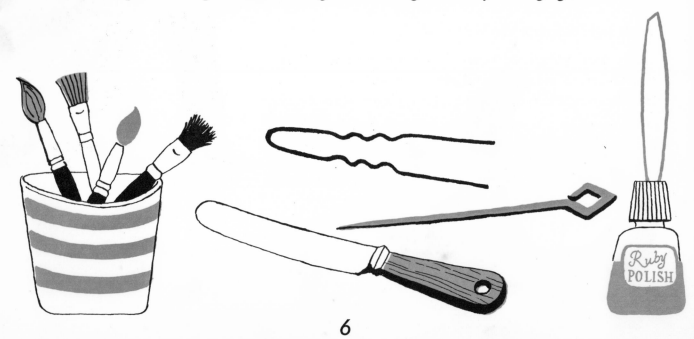

Make Some Clay Forms

Always try to make a clay object from one piece. (There will be less danger of parts falling off when the clay dries.) If cracks appear while you're working it means that the clay is too dry. Wet your fingers and smooth the clay or brush a damp sponge over it. If you need to attach parts to a form, dampen the surfaces that are to be joined and press them together. You can also use toothpicks to reinforce legs of animals and other extra parts to a form.

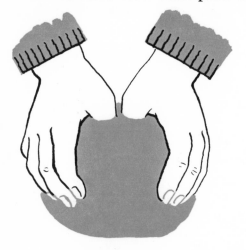

Roll the clay between your hands to make a ball. Small balls can be made into eggs, large balls can be made into pinch pots. To make a pinch pot, press your two thumbs into the center of the ball with the rest of your fingers cupped around the outside. Rotate the ball, pushing gently from within with your thumbs, and from the outside with your fingers.

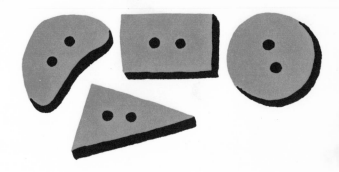

Pat the clay to flatten it. Flattened clay can be cut with a tool and made into buttons. While the clay is soft, poke two holes in the center with a toothpick.

Squeeze the clay in your hand. Squeezed clay shapes can be made into free-form ashtrays. Punch your fist into the center of a squeezed clay shape to make a hollow for ashes.

Poke, Pull and Cut

Poke the clay with your finger. A clay ball with a finger poked into one end for a mouth can become a blowfish. To complete the blowfish add a small clay form for his dorsal fin and two small balls for his eyes. Poke your pinky into the center of each eye to make the eyeballs. Press the curved end of a hairpin into the body to make the scales.

Pull the clay with your hands. Pulled clay can be made into animals. Make the surface of your animal rough—like a Ducky-Bird—or smooth, like a cat. You can stick things into your animal such as bottle caps, feathers, marbles, pipe cleaners, toothpicks, or anything else you like.

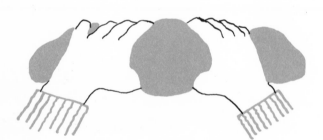

Cut the clay with a tool or dull knife. Thick slices of clay can be cut with cookie cutters to make wall plaques or paper weights. In making a wall plaque, be sure to poke a hole in the top of the form while the clay is still soft, so that it can be hung when completed.

Model Some Fruits and Vegetables

AN APPLE

WHAT YOU NEED: Clay . . . paint . . . liquid wax

WHAT YOU DO: Break off a piece of clay about the size of your fist. Roll the clay between your hands to make a ball. Press in the top to make a little hollow. Roll a small piece of clay between your hands to make a stem. Flatten a piece of clay and cut out two leaves. Wet the end of the stem and the hollow in the ball. Press the stem into the hollow. Wet the ends of the leaves and press them into the stem. When the clay is dry paint the apple. When the apple is dry pour liquid wax over it.

A CARROT

WHAT YOU NEED: Clay . . . pointed tool . . . paint . . . liquid wax

WHAT YOU DO: Break off a piece of clay about the size of your fist. Roll the clay between your hands until it becomes cigar-shaped. Pat one end into a rounded point. Press in the top of the thick end to make a little hollow. Roll small pieces of clay between your hands to make leaves. Wet the end of the leaf stems and the hollow in the shape. Press the stems into the hollow. While the clay is still soft, press small lines into the carrot with a pointed tool. When the clay is dry paint the carrot. When the carrot is dry, pour liquid wax over it.

A PINEAPPLE

WHAT YOU NEED: Clay . . . pointed tool . . . paint . . . liquid wax

WHAT YOU DO: Break off a piece of clay about twice the size of your fist. Roll the clay between your hands to make an egg-shaped ball. Press in the top to make a little hollow. Flatten a piece of clay and cut out three long pointed leaves with a tool. Wet the wide ends of the leaves and the hollow in the ball. Press the leaves into the hollow. While the clay is still soft, make criss-cross lines all over the ball with a pointed tool. Press a small hole in the center of each criss-crossed box with a tool point. When the clay is dry paint the pineapple. When the pineapple is dry pour liquid wax over it.

Some Clay-Plus Animals

You can make all kinds of realistic or imaginary animals out of clay plus other items you can find around the house such as whole cloves, marbles, toothpicks, pipe cleaners, bottle caps, feathers and so on.

A SPIDER

WHAT YOU NEED: Clay... rubber bands... liquid wax... scissors... paint

WHAT YOU DO: Make a ball for the body. Flatten the ball slightly at the bottom. Pull out a small piece at one end for the head. Cut four rubber bands in half to make eight pieces for the legs. Press the legs into the body, four on each side. Cut another rubber band in half to make one long piece. Press one end into the top of the body. When the spider is dry, paint the body and head yellow. When the paint is dry paint wide black stripes around the body, and features on the head. When the spider is dry pour liquid wax over it. Grasp one end of the long rubber band and bounce the spider up and down.

A TURTLE

WHAT YOU NEED: Clay... 4 picnic forks (plastic or wood)... paint... liquid wax

WHAT YOU DO: Make a ball for the body. Flatten the ball at the bottom. Pull out a piece at one end for the head, and at the other end for the tail. Break the prong ends off the picnic forks for legs. Press the legs into the body, two on each side. When the turtle is dry paint the shell in alternating brown and green squares and paint on the features. When the paint is dry pour liquid wax over it.

10

A GIRAFFE

WHAT YOU NEED: Clay...whole cloves...paints...liquid wax

WHAT YOU DO: Roll a thick clay coil and bend it to form the body and legs in one piece. Roll a long medium-thick coil for the neck and head. Bend and shape the head end to make the nose and mouth. Flatten two tiny clay balls for the ears. Roll a long thin coil for the mane. Bend and shape the coil like a running snake. Roll a tiny clay cigar shape for the tail. Wet all the parts you want to join, and push them firmly in place. Rub your finger over the parts where they join until the crack disappears. When the clay is dry paint the giraffe yellow. When the paint is dry paint on the features and round spots all over the body with brown paint. Press two whole cloves into the top of the head for horns. Pour liquid wax over the giraffe.

A SEAL

WHAT YOU NEED: Clay . . . marble . . . paints . . . liquid wax

WHAT YOU DO: Roll a thick clay coil. Squeeze, twist, bend and pull the coil to make the seal shape. Pull out and shape the flippers and hind limbs. Press a marble into the top of the seal's nose to make a little hollow. Remove the marble. When the clay is dry paint the seal black. When the paint is dry pour liquid wax over it and replace the marble on the seal's nose.

A PIG

WHAT YOU NEED: Clay . . . kitchen matches . . . pipe cleaner . . . paints . . . liquid wax . . . scissors

WHAT YOU DO: Roll a large egg-shaped ball. Pull out one end of the ball to make the pig's snout. Pull out and pinch two small ears at the top of the head. Cut a six-inch piece of pipe cleaner, and wind it around your finger to make a corkscrew coil. Press one end of the coil into the pig's body for the tail. Press four matchsticks into the body for legs. When the clay is dry paint the pig pink. When the paint is dry paint blue irregular spots all over the body. When the pig is dry pour liquid wax over it.

Make a Clay Bead Necklace

Clay beads are fun to make and easy, too. When the beads are dry you can paint designs on them. You can also press designs into them with a tool while they are soft, or you can make raised designs on them by adding tiny dots. You can string beads of the same shape together; you can combine beads of different shapes, or you can space small glass beads between clay beads.

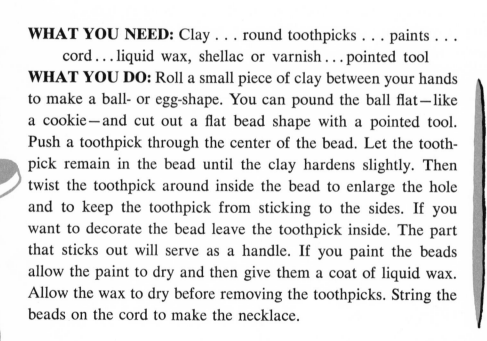

WHAT YOU NEED: Clay . . . round toothpicks . . . paints . . . cord . . . liquid wax, shellac or varnish . . . pointed tool

WHAT YOU DO: Roll a small piece of clay between your hands to make a ball- or egg-shape. You can pound the ball flat—like a cookie—and cut out a flat bead shape with a pointed tool. Push a toothpick through the center of the bead. Let the toothpick remain in the bead until the clay hardens slightly. Then twist the toothpick around inside the bead to enlarge the hole and to keep the toothpick from sticking to the sides. If you want to decorate the bead leave the toothpick inside. The part that sticks out will serve as a handle. If you paint the beads allow the paint to dry and then give them a coat of liquid wax. Allow the wax to dry before removing the toothpicks. String the beads on the cord to make the necklace.

and a Papier-mâché Santa Claus Ball

Papier-mâché is an exciting new craft material which you can make yourself. The words papier-mâché are French and mean chewed paper. You can make a lot of papier-mâché and use it to build large animals, birds, or anything else you like.

PAPIER-MÂCHÉ

WHAT YOU NEED: Old newspapers . . . ½ pound bag of wallpaper paste (buy it in paint supply stores) . . . water . . . oilcloth or plastic . . . bowl or pan

WHAT YOU DO: Cover your work table with oilcloth or plastic. Wet several sheets of newspaper and squeeze out all the water you can. Tear the paper into thumb-size bits and place them in a bowl. Sprinkle about a cup of wallpaper paste over them and mix the mass with your hand so that the paste is on most of the pieces. Add a little water at a time and squeeze the paper through your fingers. Keep squeezing until the paper is mushy and sticks together. The mass should feel slippery. If it doesn't add more paste.

SANTA CLAUS BALL

WHAT YOU NEED: Papier-mâché . . . paints (showcard or poster) . . . a screw eye for hanging . . . absorbent cotton

WHAT YOU DO: Form a big mass of papier-mâché into a ball with a point at the top. Pat the ball with your hands to make it smooth. Press the screw eye into the point for hanging. Place the ball in a warm place to dry. In about a week you will find that the ball has become very hard and is much lighter to lift. This is because the paste has dried out and the water has all evaporated. Paint Santa's face pink and his hat red. When the paint has dried paste on absorbent cotton for the hat trimming, eyebrows, moustache and beard. Hang the ball from a branch of a Christmas tree, in a window, or from an open doorway.

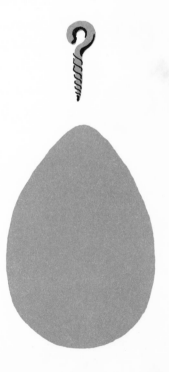

A Crêpe-Paper Clay Bowl

Crêpe-paper clay is a modeling mixture made of crêpe-paper and water. You can make all kinds of small objects from this clay such as ashtrays, nut bowls, candy dishes, wall plaques and so on.

CRÊPE-PAPER CLAY

WHAT YOU NEED: Crêpe-paper . . . 1 tablespoon salt . . . 1 cup flour . . . water . . . oilcloth or plastic . . . bowl or pan

WHAT YOU DO: Cover your work table with oilcloth or plastic. Tear the crêpe-paper into tiny confetti-size pieces and place them in the bowl. Add just enough water to cover the crêpe-paper and let it soak for about fifteen minutes until soft. Then drain off the excess water. Mix the flour and salt together. Add enough flour-salt mixture to the crêpe-paper to make a stiff dough. Knead the mixture with your hands until it is all blended together.

CRÊPE-PAPER CLAY BOWL

WHAT YOU NEED: Crêpe-paper clay . . . bowl or dish to use as a mold . . . waxed paper . . . Scotch tape . . . poster paints . . . clear shellac

WHAT YOU DO: Turn the bowl you are using for a mold upside down and cover it with waxed paper. Fasten the waxed paper inside the bowl with small pieces of Scotch tape to hold it in place. Spread a thick layer of clay over the bowl and press it down firmly and smoothly around the mold with your hands. Place it in a warm dry place for a day or two to harden. Then remove the clay bowl from the mold and paint it. When the paint has dried give it a coat of shellac. This will give the bowl a high gloss and preserve it.

A FLEET OF SOAP SHIPS

Soap is an exciting material to work with. It's inexpensive, too, because there is no waste. Mother can use the scraps you cut away, she can even use the things you make when you get tired of them. After you have made some ships like the ones in the picture you might like to make a soap fish, bird, animal, or just a nice smooth shape.

WHAT YOU NEED: Floating soap (large and small cakes) . . . sipper straws . . . thin paper . . . paints or crayons . . . blunt knife . . . orange stick . . . scissors

WHAT YOU DO: Mark off one end of a large cake of soap with an orange stick for the bow. Cut away the marked-off section with a knife. Polish and rub it smooth with the palm of your hand. Cut or tear pieces of paper into different shapes for the flags and sails. Decorate them with paints. Punch holes at the top and bottom of each. Run a sipper straw through the sails and flags for a flagpole. Press the flagpole into the bow end of the ship. Press a small flagpole and flag into the stern, or back end of the ship. Float the ships in the bathtub.

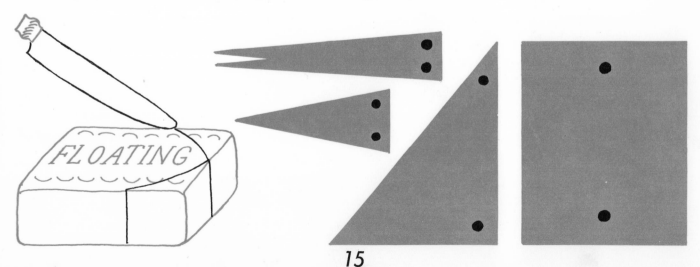

A Cork Alligator

Corks come in all shapes and sizes, and most homes have lots of them around. They can be cut or sliced; colored with tempera paint; joined together with hairpins or wire; pasted on top of each other; and they can be made to float in water. When it is necessary to cut a slit in a cork, or cut a wedge from it, you will need the help of an older person.

WHAT YOU NEED: 5 corks of different sizes...hairpins or wire...4 thumbtacks ...tempera paint...stiff paper...2 pins or tacks with colored heads...paste ...knife...scissors

WHAT YOU DO: Save the largest cork for the head and the smallest one for the tail. String the rest of the corks together with wire. Cut a small wedge for a mouth out of the narrow end of the large cork you saved for the head. Press the two pins into the cork for eyes. Cut a narrow strip of paper for the tongue and paint it red. Cut a long narrow strip of paper for the tail. With your scissors, cut a jagged edge along one long side of the tail and paint it yellow. Cut a slit in the narrow end of the small cork you saved for the tail. Insert the paper tail into the slit and fasten it to the end of the alligator. Paint a red, uneven mouth line on the head cork and paste the paper tongue inside the mouth. Fasten the head to the front of the alligator. Paint the alligator's body green. When the paint is dry, paint yellow spots on the body and press in the thumbtack legs.

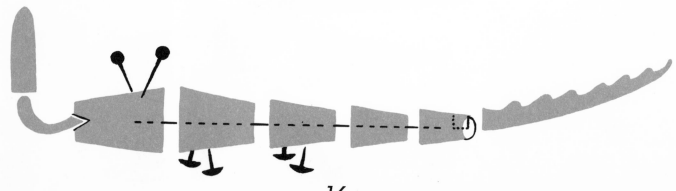

and a Family of Swans

You can have lots of fun making this mother swan and her baby swans. And after you have made them you can float them in a basin or shallow pan of water. When you float them try not to get their heads and tails wet.

WHAT YOU NEED: Corks of different sizes . . . stiff paper . . . pencil . . . thumbtacks . . . paints or crayons . . . knife . . . scissors

WHAT YOU DO: Cut two slits in each cork, one at the wide end and the other at the narrow end as shown by the dotted line. On a piece of paper draw the mother swan's head and neck in one piece and cut it out. Draw and cut out a paper tail. Paint in the eyes and beak. Slip the head and neck piece into the slit at the wide end of the cork. Slip the tail piece into the slit at the narrow end. Paint or draw the swan's wings on the cork. Push two thumbtacks into the middle of the body for feet. Make the baby swans the same way, using smaller corks.

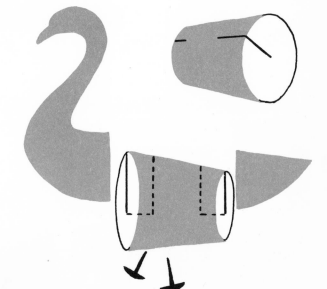

Play with Toothpicks

Most of us usually think of drawing as something that is done with pencil or crayon on paper, but you can draw with toothpicks, too. You can use whole, bent, or broken bits of toothpicks.

TOOTHPICK PICTURES

WHAT YOU NEED: Toothpicks (white or colored) . . . glue . . . construction paper (white or colored) . . . tweezers . . . pencil

WHAT YOU DO: Arrange the toothpicks on the paper to outline a figure, scene or design. Use the tweezers and move the toothpicks around until you are satisfied with the results. Then glue the toothpicks in place. Add as many pencil details as you like.

and

Toothpicks-plus

APPLE GOLLYWOG

WHAT YOU NEED: Toothpicks . . . apple . . . glue . . . paper . . . scissors

WHAT YOU DO: Stick toothpicks into the top of the apple for hair. Cut out and glue on paper features.

CENTIPEDE

WHAT YOU NEED: Toothpicks . . . string beans . . . black crayon

WHAT YOU DO: Stick broken bits of toothpicks along both sides of a string bean for legs. Draw in the eyes.

PORCUPINE

WHAT YOU NEED: Toothpicks . . . lemon . . . matchsticks . . . black crayon

WHAT YOU DO: Stick toothpicks into a lemon for the porcupine's quills. Add matchstick legs. Draw in the eyes.

Play with Paper and Paste

Paper is everywhere and many wonderful things can be made from it. There is paper that is thin or thick; shiny or dull; white, colored, patterned, metallic, soft, smooth, pebbled, grainy or lacy.

MAKE A FLOWER PICTURE

WHAT YOU NEED: Paper . . . paste . . . scissors . . . construction paper

WHAT YOU DO: Cut flower and leaf shapes from paper. Paste them in an interesting design on construction paper.

MAKE A MOSAIC PICTURE

WHAT YOU NEED: Color chips (from paint store color charts) . . . colored paper . . . scissors . . . paste . . . construction paper

WHAT YOU DO: Peel the color chips from paint store color charts, or cut small oblongs of colored paper. Paste the oblongs side by side in a colorful design on construction paper.

MAKE A STICKER PICTURE

WHAT YOU NEED: Legal seals, gummed stars, notebook reinforcements, circles, squares, oblongs, Christmas seals, gummed tape, paper lace doilies . . . scissors . . . paste . . . construction paper

WHAT YOU DO: Paste sticker seals and cut pieces of paper in a design on construction paper.

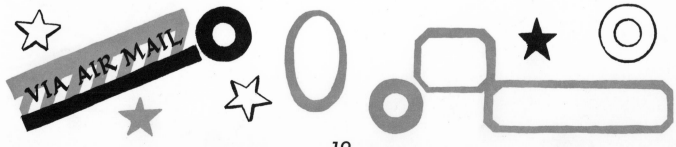

Envelope Stand-ups

You can make all kinds of animals and figures out of used or new envelopes. When you make a stand-up figure make sure to have some part of the figure on the fold of the envelope. In cutting out a stand-up figure, cut through the front and back of the envelope at the same time. Be careful not to cut on the fold.

A TENT

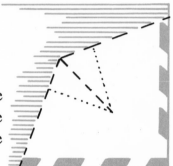

WHAT YOU NEED: Air-mail envelope . . . scissors

WHAT YOU DO: Cut the corner from the envelope following the dotted lines in the picture. Cut a slit halfway up the middle of one side. Turn back the corners to make the flaps of the tent. Press on the folded sides to make it stand.

A CAR

WHAT YOU NEED: Envelope . . . scissors . . . crayons

WHAT YOU DO: Draw the car on the envelope so that the top of the car is on the solid fold. Cut the car out and color it with crayon. Spread the wheels to make it stand.

AN ELEPHANT

WHAT YOU NEED: Envelope . . . scissors . . . crayons

WHAT YOU DO: Draw the elephant on the corner of the envelope. Cut out the elephant shape and cut away the shaded part on the head as shown in the picture. Slit on ear fold. Fold the elephant's ears down on the dotted line. Color the elephant and draw in the features. Spread the legs to make it stand.

A PINWHEEL

WHAT YOU NEED: Paper . . . thumbtack or pin . . . dowel stick or sipper straw . . . pencil . . . scissors

WHAT YOU DO: Start with a paper square. Cut from each corner of the square to the center, but not all the way. Make a dot in the center. Bend each flap to the center dot following the letters, a, b, c, and d. Stick a pin or thumbtack through the flaps in the center. Pin the pinwheel to a stick, or sipper straw, and watch it spin easily and rapidly in the breeze.

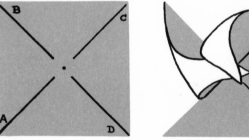

AND A DUCKY-BIRD

WHAT YOU NEED: Paper . . . pencil . . . a penny . . . paints or crayons . . . paste . . . scissors

WHAT YOU DO: Draw a bird on paper like the one in the picture. Cut out the bird and color it. Paste a penny on the underside of the bird's head. Allow the paste to dry. Balance the Ducky-bird by resting the penny on the tip of your finger, on the rim of a glass, or on some other object.

21

A PARACHUTE

WHAT YOU NEED: A paper napkin . . . string . . . small cork . . . scissors

WHAT YOU DO: Tie pieces of string, each twelve inches long, to the four corners of the napkin. Tie the other end of the strings to a small cork. Toss the parachute into the air and watch it float down gracefully. Glue a small figure to the cork if you like.

AND A JIGSAW PUZZLE

WHAT YOU NEED: Shirt cardboard (of the laundry type) . . . colorful magazine picture . . . paste . . . black crayon . . . scissors

WHAT YOU DO: Paste the magazine picture to the cardboard. Allow the paste to dry. With a crayon, divide the picture into five or six irregular sections. Cut along the crayoned lines to make the separate pieces of the puzzle. Mix up the pieces and see how long it takes you to put the jigsaw puzzle together again.

Tops That Are Tops

Tops are fun to play with at any time of the year, indoors or out. You can make all kinds of tops from cardboard, milk-bottle caps, jar lids, empty thread or typewriter spools, pop-bottle caps, acorns, coasters, or any other round object through which you can punch a hole in the center.

WHAT YOU NEED: Cardboard or stiff paper . . . pencil . . . glass, cup, or compass . . . paints or crayons . . . short pencil, lollipop stick, or meat skewer . . . scissors

WHAT YOU DO: Draw a circle on cardboard using a glass, cup, or compass as a guide. Cut the circle out and decorate it with paints or crayons. Push a pencil or stick through the center of the circle and spin the top.

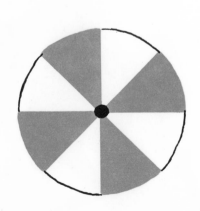

Bookmarks for

People who are always studying or reading books are called bookworms. Any bookworm would appreciate a bookmark as a gift.

PIPE CLEANER BOOKMARK

WHAT YOU NEED: White or colored pipe cleaner . . . crayons
WHAT YOU DO: Make several kinks in a pipe cleaner. Add crayon features and any other ornaments you like.

OLD GREETING CARD BOOKMARK

WHAT YOU NEED: Old greeting card . . . pencil . . . ruler . . . scissors
WHAT YOU DO: Decide what part of your greeting card you want to use for the bookmark. For best results, pick out a part that is a complete picture by itself. With a pencil and ruler, mark off the part and cut it out. Cut a curved slit near the top of the bookmark for slipping over the page, as shown by the dotted line.

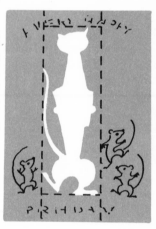

COLORED PAPER BOOKMARK

WHAT YOU NEED: Colored construction paper . . . scissors . . . fancy ribbon . . . paints or crayons
WHAT YOU DO: Cut a strip of paper about one and a half inches wide and about seven inches long. Cut two slits in the paper, one at the top and one at the bottom. Pull a piece of fancy ribbon through the slits. Decorate the bookmark with paints or crayons.

BOOKWORM BOOKMARK

WHAT YOU NEED: Colored felt . . . scissors . . . rhinestone or sequin . . . glue . . . fancy ribbon
WHAT YOU DO: Cut out a wiggly worm shape from colored felt. Glue on a rhinestone or sequin eye. Glue on a tiny piece of fancy ribbon for a collar.

Bookworms

AND A ROLY-EYED ELEPHANT

WHAT YOU NEED: Stiff paper or thin cardboard . . . 2 bottle caps . . . cellophane paper . . . Scotch tape . . . pencil . . . 2 beads or buttons . . . paints or crayons . . . scissors . . . paste

WHAT YOU DO: Draw the elephant's head on a piece of stiff paper and cut it out. For the eyes, draw two circles a little smaller than the bottle caps. Cut out the circles. Color the elephant's head with paints or crayons. When the paint is dry, turn the head over. In back of the eye holes, paste two squares of cellophane paper larger than the holes. Place a bead in the center of the cellophane square for an eyeball. Place the bottle cap over the bead and fasten with Scotch tape. Do the same with the other eye. Turn the head over and watch the elephant roll his eyes when you shake his head!

Greeting Cards

Use white or colored construction paper, thin cardboard, or stiff paper for the cards. Cut the card shapes to fit the envelopes you intend using.

Plain and Deckle-edged Cards. Cut plain cards with straight edges, or cut cards with pinking shears to make a deckle edge.

Book Folder Cards. Fold a piece of paper in half to make a book. Book folder cards can be long and narrow or short and wide, and the fold can be at the top, side or bottom.

French Fold Cards. Fold a square of paper in half, then fold it in half again. Write the message on the outside fold, the inside fold, or on the completely opened sheet.

A PUSSY WILLOW FRIENDSHIP CARD

WHAT YOU NEED: Paper . . . pussy willow bud . . . paints or crayons . . . paste . . . scissors

WHAT YOU DO: Make a plain or deckle-edge card. Paste the pussy willow bud in the center of the card. This will be the "body" of a bee. Draw or paint in the feelers, wings and legs. Write a suitable message such as "Bee My Friend."

A STRING VALENTINE'S DAY CARD

WHAT YOU NEED: Red paper . . . glue in a bottle with a dispenser tip . . . paints or crayons . . . colorless nail polish . . . glitter . . . scissors . . . pencil . . . fancy string

WHAT YOU DO: Make a red book folder card. With a pencil, lightly draw a heart shape on the outside. Go over the pencilled line with a thin line of glue. Press fancy string on the outline while the glue is wet. Paint the inside of the heart shape with colorless nail polish. While the polish is wet shake glitter over it. Allow the polish to dry and shake off the excess glitter. Write a suitable message such as "My Heart Glows for You."

for All Occasions

A NEW YEAR'S GREETING CARD

WHAT YOU NEED: Colored paper . . . paints or crayons . . . fancy ribbon . . . paste . . . scissors

WHAT YOU DO: Make a colored paper book folder. With the folded edge at the top, draw a bell shape with crayon on the outside. Cut the shape out, but do not cut into the top folded edge. Punch a hole at the top. Pull a piece of ribbon through the hole and finish off with a bow. Write a suitable message such as "Ring in the New!"

A CHRISTMAS TREE CARD

WHAT YOU NEED: Metallic or colored paper . . . white paper . . . white paint, crayon or chalk . . . scissors . . . paste . . . nail or paper punch

WHAT YOU DO: Make a metallic, plain, or deckle-edge card. Draw a Christmas-tree shape on white paper and cut it out. With a nail, or paper punch, make small holes all over the tree. Paste the paper tree on the card. The card color will show through the holes and look like tree lights. Write a suitable message in white such as "To light up your Christmas!"

A COTTON BALL EASTER CARD

WHAT YOU NEED: Gray paper . . . pink paper . . . small cotton balls . . . paste . . . scissors . . . crayons

WHAT YOU DO: Make a French fold card of gray paper. Paste three cotton balls, one under the other, on the front of the card. These will be the bunny's head, body and tail. Cut out two long pointed ears from pink paper. Paste the wide ends of the ears to the bunny's head. Draw in the bunny's whiskers, features, and decorations with crayon. Write a suitable message such as "Bunnies Bring Blessings on Easter" inside the card.

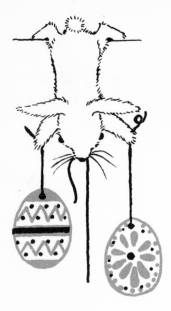

Here are some colorful decorations you can make to use on holidays, birthdays, and party days. Hang them from Christmas trees, mantelpieces, window frames, and in doorways.

GLITTER EASTER EGGS

WHAT YOU NEED: Stiff paper or thin cardboard . . . paints or crayons . . . string or ribbon . . . glue . . . glitter . . . scissors . . . string

WHAT YOU DO: Cut egg shapes from paper and decorate them with paints or crayons. Spread glue on some parts of the design and sprinkle glitter on the glue. When the glue is dry shake off the excess glitter. Make a hole at the top and pull a piece of string through the hole for hanging.

PUMPKIN FACES

WHAT YOU NEED: Orange construction paper . . . black crayon . . . string or ribbon . . . scissors

WHAT YOU DO: Cut a pumpkin shape from paper. Draw in the eyes, nose and mouth with black crayon. Pull a piece of string through a hole at the top for hanging.

RING CHAINS

WHAT YOU NEED: Fancy or colored paper . . . paste . . . scissors

WHAT YOU DO: Cut paper into narrow strips. Fold a strip into a circle and paste the ends together to make a ring. Slip another strip through the ring and paste the ends together. Continue until the ring chain is as long as you want.

RING AND STRAW GARLANDS

WHAT YOU NEED: Colored construction paper . . . colored sipper straws . . . compass . . . scissors . . . string

WHAT YOU DO: Cut circles of the same size from colored paper and make a hole in the center of each. Cut small pieces of sipper straws. String circles and straws on string.

All Occasions

HANGING DECORATION

WHAT YOU NEED: Colored construction paper . . . string or ribbon . . . compass . . . large beads . . . scissors

WHAT YOU DO: Draw and cut out three circles of different sizes from paper. Run a string through the circles, with the largest one at the top and the smallest one at the bottom and with beads in between.

3-D COLORFUL BALLS

WHAT YOU NEED: Colored construction paper . . . string or ribbon . . . compass . . . scissors

WHAT YOU DO: Cut two colored paper circles of the same size. Make a slit in one paper circle, from the top down, half way to the center. Make a slit in the other paper circle, from the bottom up, half way to the center. Put the circles together by slipping one slit into the other. Pull a piece of string through a hole at the top for hanging.

POWDER PUFF ANGEL

WHAT YOU NEED: Pink powder puff . . . metallic paper . . . yellow construction paper . . . glue . . . crayons . . . white or yellow pipe cleaner . . . scissors

WHAT YOU DO: Draw a face on the powder puff with crayons. Cut a pair of metallic wings and glue them to the back of the powder puff. Cut a yellow paper fringe for hair and glue it to the forehead. Bend a pipe cleaner into a halo shape and glue it to the back of the head.

PAPER LANTERNS

WHAT YOU NEED: Colored construction paper . . . ruler . . . glue . . . scissors

WHAT YOU DO: Cut a strip of paper 12 inches long and about 6 inches wide. Fold the strip down the center the long way. With scissors, make evenly-spaced slashes from the folded edge almost across the paper. Glue the ends together. Glue a strip of paper across the top of the lantern for hanging.

A Paper Collage

A collage is a picture which is made by gluing different kinds of materials together to form a design. The collage on this page is made entirely of paper, but you can make a collage using pipe cleaners, toothpicks, sipper straws, wire mesh, sequins, rubber bands, cloth scraps, tinfoil, cellophane, gummed labels, feathers, corks, yarn, ribbon, or anything else you wish.

WHAT YOU NEED: Paper of all kinds and textures . . . glue . . . pencil . . . scissors . . . construction paper

WHAT YOU DO: Draw on construction paper a large outline picture of a fish, an animal, flower, bird, or anything else that appeals to you. Cut or tear large and small shapes from different kinds of paper. Spread a thin layer of glue over the drawing, keeping it within the outline. Place the paper shapes all over the picture while the glue is wet. Trim any pieces that extend beyond the drawing.

You can weave simple, one-over-one-under paper mats of two colors, or you can make other designs by weaving the strips differently and using paper of several different colors.

WHAT YOU NEED: Colored papers ... pencil ... ruler ... scissors

WHAT YOU DO: Fold a square of paper in half. Starting at the folded edge, draw evenly-spaced lines, not quite to the edge, with a ruler and pencil. Cut carefully along the pencilled lines. Now cut single strips from paper of a different color. Weave the single strips, *over* one and under one, all the way across the paper mat. Start the second strip *under* one and over one, all the way across the mat. Weave different designs using several colors.

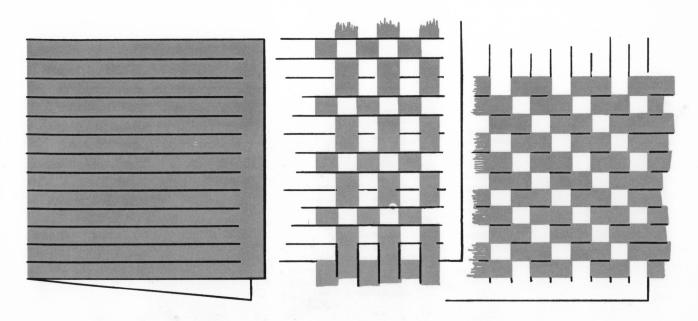

Knights lived many years ago during a period in history known as the Medieval Period. A young boy who was chosen as a knight-to-be was sent to the court of some great prince or duke. There he learned how to ride, how to use weapons, and how to be obedient and courteous.

WHAT YOU NEED: 3 shirt cardboards (of the laundry type)...string...aluminum foil...Scotch tape...glue...paints or crayons...pencil...scissors

WHAT YOU DO: *Visor*. Draw the visor shape on a shirt cardboard. Cut away the shaded part and make two holes for tying. *Knight's Cross*. Draw a cross on aluminum foil. Cut away the shaded area. Glue the cross to the center of the visor. Pull string through the holes in the visor for tying. Make another cross the same way and save it to glue on the shield. *Sword*. Draw the sword shape on a shirt cardboard. Cut away the shaded area. Decorate the hilt of the sword with paints or crayons. *Shield*. Draw the shield shape on a shirt cardboard. Cut away the shaded area. Paste the second cross to the center of the shield. Turn the shield over and, for a handle, fasten a narrow strip of cardboard to the back with Scotch tape.

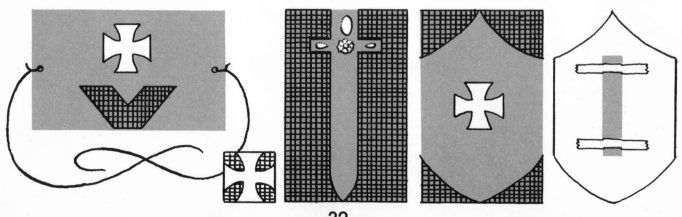

Booklets and Folders

You can use these little booklets and folders as scrap books, hobbybooks, writing and drawing books, and as photograph albums.

BOOKLETS

WHAT YOU NEED: Sheets of paper of the same size . . . heavy thread or cord . . . darning needle . . . nail . . . scissors

WHAT YOU DO: Fold several sheets of paper down the center. Use the nail to punch two holes on the fold through all thicknesses of the paper. Then, with a darning needle and heavy thread, and beginning on the inside of the book, push the needle through to the outside, leaving about three inches of thread inside the book. Bring the needle back through the other hole to the center. Pull the thread tight and tie in a knot.

FOLDERS

WHAT YOU NEED: Paper . . . scissors

WHAT YOU DO: Cut a long strip of paper of any length and width. Accordion-pleat the strip to make a long fold-up folder.

Stabile Space Design

Stabile space designs are objects that are stationary and don't move. They can be seen everywhere. Examples are television aerials on rooftops, bridges across rivers, even fences in backyards. All these things have parts, and spaces between and around the parts. The parts make a design surrounded by space. Make a space design for an ornament or just for fun.

WHAT YOU NEED: Clay...stiff and straight things such as ice cream sticks, lollipop sticks, meat skewers, forks, sipper straws, picnic forks, etc....things that bend such as wire, pipe cleaners, yarn, string, rubber bands, etc....small things such as corks, bottle tops, shells, keys, stones, paper clips, acorns, etc.... glue...scissors

WHAT YOU DO: Shape the clay into a ball for a base. Stick all kinds of things into the base, things that bend and things that don't bend. Glue or fasten small objects to the things stuck in the base. Push things into the clay base, too. Look at your stabile from all sides. Make it look interesting and balanced.

Mobile Space Design

Mobile space designs are objects that move. They're called space designs (just like stabiles) because they have spaces around and between the parts. They're called mobiles because they have motion. The most important thing about a mobile is its motion. You can make a standing mobile that has little motion, or a hanging mobile that has lots of motion.

WHAT YOU NEED: Thin cardboard or heavy paper . . . fancy wrapping paper, old greeting cards, colored paper, tinfoil, etc. . . . string . . . glue . . . pencil . . . nail . . . ruler . . . scissors

WHAT YOU DO: Cut a strip of cardboard about four inches wide and about twenty-four inches long. Glue the ends together to make a circle. Make holes around the bottom edge of the circle with a nail. Cut strips or shapes of fancy papers, or cards, of different sizes. Make a small hole at the end of each shape. Pull pieces of string through the holes in the strips and hang them from the holes in the cardboard circle. Make four holes at the top of the cardboard circle and attach strings for hanging. Hang the mobile from a ceiling light fixture, or in an open doorway or window, where it will be free to move in the breeze.

Paper Magics

Paper magics (and paper sculpture) are shaped paper forms. You can do all kinds of interesting things with a piece of paper. You can make pleats in it by folding it back and forth like an accordion. You can crumple and squeeze it to make a new texture. You can cut an edge to make a fringe. You can tear the edge to make a ragged finish. You can curl any fringed or ragged edge by pulling it over a closed pair of scissors. You can wind strips around a pencil to make corkscrew curls. You can bend and fasten it to make a cone, tent, or tepee. You can make cuts and tears in it and fold back little flaps. You can slash, twist and turn loose pieces to make them stand away from the background. You can punch holes in paper and peek through it. You can make paper magics that may remind you of an animal, fish, bird, or just a form, or design.

WHAT YOU NEED: Construction, typewriter, wrapping or stiff paper . . . glue . . . clips, fasteners or pins . . . scissors

WHAT YOU DO: Start with a paper square, circle, triangle, strip or irregular shape. Cut, tear, twist, pleat, crumple, curl, fringe, bend or punch holes in it. Use glue, clips, fasteners or pins to shape your paper magics as you wish.

Paper Magics-plus

You can make different kinds of paper magics by combining paper forms with other items such as cardboard scraps, candy papers, cardboard tubes, paper cones, small boxes, picnic plates, and so forth.

A BIRD ON THE WING

WHAT YOU NEED: Paper . . . pencil . . . scissors
WHAT YOU DO: Cut a simple bird shape out of paper. Cut a slot in back of the head of the bird. For the wings, cut a strip of paper and pleat it like an accordion. Slip the pleated paper into the slot in back of the head.

A BUTTERFLY ON A LIMB

WHAT YOU NEED: Paper . . . pencil . . . paints or crayons . . .
   clothespin . . . scissors . . . glue
WHAT YOU DO: Fold a piece of paper in half. Draw the butterfly's wing along the folded edge. Cut out the wing shape but do not cut into the fold. Open the wings. Glue a clothespin to the center of the wings to make the body. Decorate the wings on both sides with paints or crayons. Clip the butterfly to a branch or clothesline.

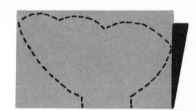

MAILING TUBE CANDLESTICK

WHAT YOU NEED: Cardboard tube . . . picnic plate . . . glue . . .
   paints or crayons . . . scissors . . . paper
WHAT YOU DO: Cut four small slits in one end of the tube. Spread the slits and glue the tube to the middle of the picnic plate. Cut a small piece of paper for a flame and color it red. Glue the "flame" inside the tube. Decorate the plate with paints or crayons.

Paper Bag Masks

Masks are fun to make because they don't have to look like real faces at all. They can be funny, sad, scary, silly, young or old. You can decorate your masks with paints, crayons, chalk or ink. You can glue extra parts on your masks such as yarn, feathers, absorbent cotton, sipper straws, bottle caps, toothpicks, candy papers, and so forth. Make masks for special parties, holidays, plays, or just for the fun of pretending to be someone else.

A PAPER BAG MASK

WHAT YOU NEED: Paper bag to fit over your head . . . chalk, paints or crayons . . .
    glue . . . scissors . . . things to glue on
WHAT YOU DO: Slip the bag over your head. With a finger rubbed in chalk, mark the eye, nose and mouth locations on the bag. Take the bag off and decorate it in any way you please. Cut out the eye holes.

A TIE-ON MASK

WHAT YOU NEED: Paper . . . scissors . . . crayons . . . string
WHAT YOU DO: Cut a mask shape from paper large enough to cover your face. Attach strings to the sides for tying. Cut out the eye holes and decorate the mask as you please.

A STUFFED HEAD MASK

WHAT YOU NEED: Paper bag . . . paints or crayons . . . newspapers . . .
    string . . . long stick, dowel or sink mop
WHAT YOU DO: Turn the bag upside down so that the opening is at the bottom. Draw or paint any kind of a face on the mask. Push a long stick into the open end of the bag. (The piece that sticks out will serve as a handle.) Stuff the "head" with newspapers and tie it at the bottom with a piece of string.

Paper Bag Puppets

Puppets are little doll-like figures that can be made to act as you want them to. The animal puppets on this page will perform for you, but you must do the talking for them.

A PAPER BAG PUSSY CAT

WHAT YOU NEED: Paper bag to fit over your hand . . . sipper straws or broom straws . . . crayons . . . scissors

WHAT YOU DO: Turn the bag so that the fold is at the top. Draw the pussy cat's face and decorations on one side of the bag with crayons. Push sipper or broom straws into the face for whiskers. Make two holes at the top of the bag above the face. Put your hand in the bag and push your two fingers up through the holes for ears. Wiggle your fingers to make the pussy cat's ears move.

A PAPER BAG PUPPY DOG

WHAT YOU NEED: #4 paper bag with a square bottom . . . paper . . . glue . . . paints or crayons . . . scissors

WHAT YOU DO: Turn the bag upside down so that the square fold is at the top. Draw the puppy's features on the folded flat part of the bag. Open the fold and draw the puppy's tongue under the bottom fold and part of the way down the front of the bag. Cut out two paper ears and glue them to the back of the head. Slip your hand inside the bag and curl your fingers over the fold. Open and close your fingers and the puppy will open and close his mouth.

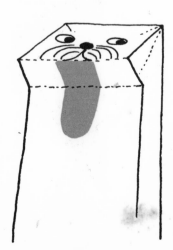
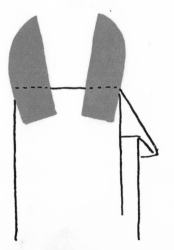

Grocery Carton Puppet Theater

You don't need a real theater in order to put on a puppet show. Here's one you can make with a little help from an older person.

WHAT YOU NEED: Large grocery carton . . . scrap cloth . . . glue . . . paints or crayons . . . scissors . . . knife

WHAT YOU DO: Have an older person cut away the top, bottom, and one long side of the grocery carton. You will have a folding-type screen with one long side and two short sides left. Cut a window in the center of the long side for the stage opening. Cut out a pair of curtains from scrap cloth and glue them inside the theater at the sides of the opening. Print the name of the theater at the top and add as many decorations as you like. Now put on a puppet show!

Play with Paint

COLOR IS EXCITING

There are many colors you can use:

    ...warm, bright colors such as red, orange and yellow

    ...cool, bright colors such as blue, green and purple

    ...soft, soothing colors such as gray, beige and moss green

    ...and other wonderfully exciting colors that you can mix yourself

Paint a picture of something you like, in any way you like. There is no one way to paint. There are many ways to paint. There is *your* way to paint.

Draw with Crayons

Use any kind of wax crayons in standard or jumbo sizes.

MAKE A CRAYON-ETCHED PICTURE

WHAT YOU NEED: Construction paper . . . crayons . . . toothpick, nail or any pointed tool

WHAT YOU DO: Cover the whole paper with crayon strokes. Use crayon of one color or many colors. Now, right over the colored crayon strokes, cover the whole paper with black crayon strokes. Scratch a picture through the black crayon coating with a pointed tool. You will see the colors underneath shine through the scratches.

MAKE A WALL PICTURE, OR MURAL

WHAT YOU NEED: Large sheet of wrapping paper . . . crayons . . . pencil

WHAT YOU DO: Sketch a picture on wrapping paper with a pencil. Draw in different parts of the picture with colored crayon. Fill in some parts of the picture with solid strokes and leave other parts of the picture in outline.

Work with Wet Chalk

Chalk pictures will not last as long as crayon pictures, but with chalk you can erase mistakes easily, and get interesting color combinations by blending colors together with your finger.

WET CHALK PICTURES

WHAT YOU NEED: Colored construction paper . . . white and colored chalk . . .
   pencil . . . sponge . . . water

WHAT YOU DO: Plan your picture before you start. Decide on the effect you want to get. Then lightly sketch in the picture with a pencil. Dampen the paper with a wet sponge. Fill in parts of the picture with solid strokes of chalk and leave other parts of the picture in outline.

   Here are some interesting effects you might like to try
      . . . colored chalk on white or colored paper
      . . . black and white chalk on black, white or gray paper
      . . . white chalk on black or dark colored paper

Play with Finger Paints

MOTHER'S HOMEMADE FINGER PAINT

Mix 1 cup of flour, ½ cup of sugar, and 1 cup of water together. Pour 3 cups of boiling water into the top of a double boiler and add the above mixture. Cook and stir until thick. Remove from the flame and add 1 tablespoon of boric acid and several drops of oil of cloves. Divide into portions and add powdered paint for coloring.

MAKE A FINGER PAINTING

WHAT YOU NEED: Finger paints . . . finger-paint paper or glazed shelf paper . . . old newspapers . . . smock or apron . . . water . . . shallow pan

WHAT YOU DO:

1) Soak the paper in a pan of water so that both sides are wet. Press the paper smooth on a table.
2) Pour some finger paint in the center of the paper.
3) Smooth the paint over the entire surface of the paper with the palm of your hand.
4) Use your fist in a swirling motion.
5) Use your knuckles or fingers in a wavy motion.
6) Use the side of your hand or fingers in a zig-zag motion.
7) Use your fingernails in a scratching motion.

PLACE YOUR FINISHED PICTURE ON A NEWSPAPER PAD TO DRY.

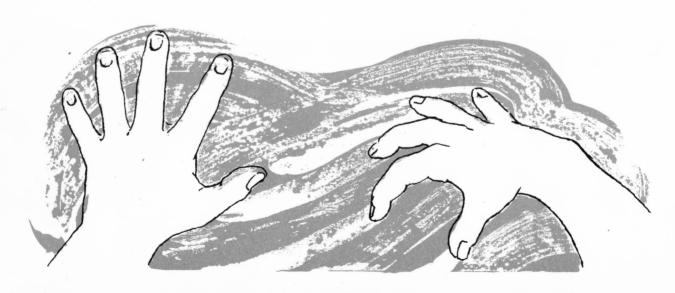

Things To Do with Finger Paintings

FINGER PAINTINGS UNDER CUT-OUTS

WHAT YOU NEED: Finger paintings . . . black construction paper
. . . glue . . . pencil . . . scissors

WHAT YOU DO: Draw a simple outline picture of a leaf, bell, flower or design on the black construction paper with pencil. Cut the picture out of the paper. The paper from which the picture was cut is the cut-out. Now glue the cut-out over a finger painting.

BAND-AID BOX CIGARETTE CASE

WHAT YOU NEED: Finger painting . . . empty Band-aid box . . .
glue . . . ruler . . . scissors . . . pencil

WHAT YOU DO: Measure and cut a strip of finger-paint decorated paper as wide as the box and a little longer than is needed to go around the box for lapping. Measure and cut a piece of decorated paper for the top. Spread a thin layer of glue around the box, including the top. Glue the small piece to the top of the box and the long piece around the box.

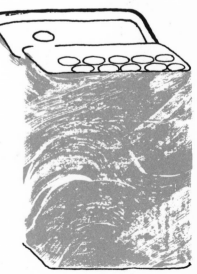

Press Time

Ends of sticks, spools, corks, carrots, bolts, nuts, screws, or any small object of unusual shape having one flat side can all be used to print many patterns. Also, different shapes can be cut from the ends of potatoes, carrots, corks, and erasers.

MAKE AN INKING PAD

WHAT YOU NEED: Paper toweling . . . water color, ink, dye or paint . . . shallow dish . . . paper or cloth

WHAT YOU DO: Place water-color paint in a shallow dish. Make a pad of several thicknesses of paper toweling and place it over the paint. Let the paint soak through the pad. Press the items on the pad for "inking." Print on paper or cloth.

MAKE A PATTERN PRINT

WHAT YOU NEED: Printing items . . . inking pad . . . paper or cloth

WHAT YOU DO: Experiment with different designs, combinations of shapes, and colors. See what forms and colors look most attractive next to each other. Use pattern prints for wrapping papers, book covers, place mats, and for covering small gift boxes, lamp shades, wastepaper baskets and so forth.

Print Time

Letters are a combination of straight and curved lines. The straight lines are sometimes vertical (parallel to the sides of the page), sometimes horizontal (parallel to the top and bottom of the page). Sometimes they are slanted. You will be using letters all your life.

PRINT THE ALPHABET

WHAT YOU NEED: Ruled paper . . . crayons, chalk or beginner's pencils
WHAT YOU DO: Study the letters below. See which are straight-line letters; slant-line letters; curved letters; and which are a combination of straight and curved lines. Print the letters of the alphabet on paper. Have some older person show you the letters that make up your name. Print the letters that make up your name.

Pictures To Make

SCRIBBLE PICTURES

WHAT YOU NEED: Paper . . . pencil . . . crayons

WHAT YOU DO: Place the pencil at any point on the paper and start to scribble. Cover the whole paper with scribble marks. Look at your scribblings from all sides. See if any part reminds you of something in particular. Then outline that part in black crayon, or fill in the part with colored crayon. If you like, you can just fill in small areas with crayons of several different colors to make a design.

CHALK BLOT PICTURES

WHAT YOU NEED: Paper . . . wallpaper paste (buy it in a paint supply store) . . . colored chalks

WHAT YOU DO: Fold the paper in half lengthwise. Open the paper out flat. Dip colored chalk in wallpaper paste and apply large dabs of chalk-paint in different colors on the fold. Fold the paper again and smooth it with your hands from the fold out. Open the paper and see the colorful picture you have made!

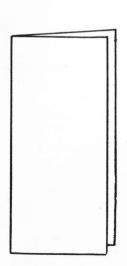
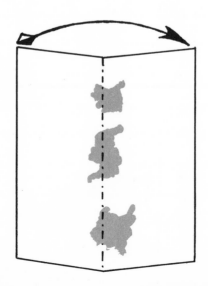
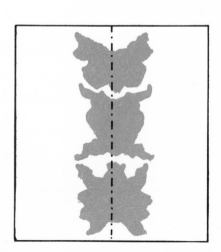

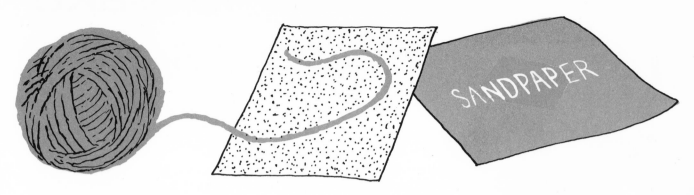

SANDPAPER AND YARN PICTURES

WHAT YOU NEED: Sheet of coarse sandpaper . . . heavy cardboard . . . colored
   yarn . . . glue . . . scissors

WHAT YOU DO: Glue the sheet of sandpaper to the cardboard. Make an outline
picture on the sandpaper background with pieces of colored yarn. The yarn will
stick to the sandpaper. If you want to make changes in your picture as you go along,
or when you're ready to make a new one, just pull the yarn away from the sandpaper.

AND SCISSOR-BEAK PICTURES

WHAT YOU NEED: Paper . . . crayons . . . scissors

WHAT YOU DO: Draw a simple outline picture of an animal or bird without its
beak. Push the points of the scissors through the paper where the animal's beak
should be, as shown by the dotted line. Place your hand behind the picture and
grasp the handle of the scissors. Open and close the scissor points and the animal
will move his beak!

Feeling and Seeing Pictures

Did you know that you can "see" with your hands as well as with your eyes? Well, you can. Try it. Close your eyes and run your hand over something scratchy, like sandpaper, or something smooth, like satin; something cold like an ice cube, or something wet, like a damp sponge. By feeling these things with your hands you are also able to "see" them.

WHAT YOU NEED: Materials that are soft and smooth such as silk, fur scraps, satin, wool, shiny paper, yarn, etc.... materials that are rough—sandpaper, corrugated cardboard, egg crate liners, etc.... materials that have texture—string, paper lace doilies, patterned paper, etc.... materials you can look through—orange sacks, lace, mosquito netting, etc.... heavy paper or thin cardboard...glue...scissors

WHAT YOU DO: Choose things that have a special kind of texture. Cut or tear these materials into shapes that please you. Arrange the pieces on a cardboard background. You can put some materials that you can see through on top of others if it makes your picture more interesting. Move the pieces around until you are pleased with the result. Then fasten the pieces to the cardboard and to each other with glue.

Play with Boxes

and Containers

MILK CARTON DONKEY

WHAT YOU NEED: Empty quart milk carton . . . pink construction paper . . . paints
. . . glue . . . soap or slice of raw potato . . . scissors

WHAT YOU DO: Paint the carton brown. To make the paint stick to the waxed surface of the carton, rub your brush on soap or raw potato before putting it into the paint. Cut two pointed ears from pink paper. Glue the ears to the back of the donkey's head. Paint on the features.

CEREAL BOX FLOWER VASE

WHAT YOU NEED: Empty cereal box . . . glue . . .
aluminum foil . . . scissors

WHAT YOU DO: Have an older person cut off the top of a cereal box. Cut a piece of aluminum foil a little longer and wider than is needed to go around the box. Spread a light coat of glue over the box. Press the aluminum foil around the box, tucking the top edge into the box. Glue down the open edge. Place artificial flowers or leaves in the vase.

A MEXICAN BALERO GAME

WHAT YOU NEED: ½ pint milk carton...string...nail... doughnut-shape hardware washer

WHAT YOU DO: Have an older person cut off the top of a milk carton as shown by the dotted lines. Punch a hole on each side of the carton with a nail. Knot the doughnut washer in the center of a 20-inch long piece of string. Bring the ends of the string up through the holes in the carton and knot the ends inside. To play the game, hold the balero in your hand and try to flip the washer into the open end.

A BIRD FEEDING STATION

WHAT YOU NEED: Empty quart milk carton with peaked top ...heavy string...nail...suet or fat...wild bird seeds

WHAT YOU DO: Have an older person cut a large window out of the front of the carton, as shown by the shaded area in the picture. Close the carton at the top and make a hole in the peak with a nail. Pull a piece of string through the hole. Roll a piece of suet in wild bird seeds and place it in the feeder. Hang the feeder where you can watch the birds when they come to feed.

Play with Wire

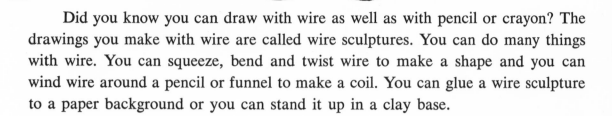

Did you know you can draw with wire as well as with pencil or crayon? The drawings you make with wire are called wire sculptures. You can do many things with wire. You can squeeze, bend and twist wire to make a shape and you can wind wire around a pencil or funnel to make a coil. You can glue a wire sculpture to a paper background or you can stand it up in a clay base.

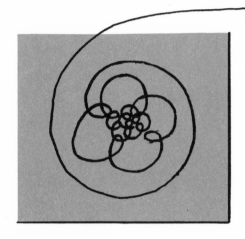

WIRE SCULPTURE WITHOUT A FORM

WHAT YOU NEED: Soft wire (soldering, picture or bell) ...colored construction paper...glue

WHAT YOU DO: Start with a piece of wire about two feet long. Hold one end, and bend it, turn it, twist it as if you were drawing an outline picture of something. Put in bumps, kinks, loops, twists and turns as you go along. When it's finished glue it to a paper background.

WIRE SCULPTURE OVER A FORM

WHAT YOU NEED: Soft wire ... clay ... pencil ... soft wood board ... hammer ... small nails

WHAT YOU DO: Draw a simple outline of an animal, bird or fish on the soft wood board. Hammer nails along the pencilled outline. Stretch wire around the nails following the outline. Lift the wire sculpture off the nails in the board without spoiling the outline. Twist the ends of the wire together, and push them into a ball of clay for a base. Stand the sculpture upright.

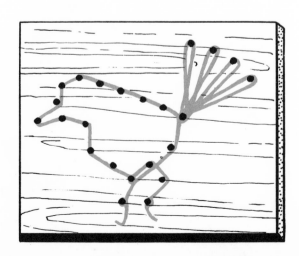

Play with Rocks and Stones

A COLLAGE PAPERWEIGHT

WHAT YOU NEED: Small stones, shells, or colored fish bowl chips (buy them in pet stores)...wallpaper cleaner (buy it in paint stores)...shellac

WHAT YOU DO: Roll two large handfuls of wallpaper cleaner into a ball. Flatten the ball at the bottom so that it will stand. Press stones, shells, and chips on all sides of the paperweight. Let the paperweight stand for several days until it is hard. Then apply a coat of shellac over the surface to make it shiny and to protect it.

A CAGED STONE NECKLACE

WHAT YOU NEED: Stone (granite, quartz, etc.) . . . soft copper wire . . . waterproof cement . . . paints . . . ribbon . . . varnish . . . scissors

WHAT YOU DO: Select as nearly perfect a stone as possible. Form a loop of wire. Place the stone inside the loop. Twist the loop several times to hold the stone securely. If it is still loose, add a little cement. Paint a design on the surface of the stone. When the paint is dry apply a thin coat of varnish. When the varnish is thoroughly dry, hang the stone from a ribbon to make the necklace.

Play with Hammer and Nails

You can make beautiful as well as useful things from wood. If you are very young or just beginning to work with wood you won't need many tools. A hammer, saw, nails, and some kind of scrap wood is all you need to start.

A BIRD NEST-BUILDING RACK

WHAT YOU NEED: 2 wooden slats, old rulers, discarded Venetian blind slats...orange mesh fruit bag...nails (roofing or fourpenny)...nesting materials such as: yarn, thread, wood shavings, paper strips, straw, dry grass, rootlets, etc....hammer...saw

WHAT YOU DO: Start with two wooden slats of the same size. They should be a little wider than the mesh fruit bag you intend using. Flatten out the mesh fruit bag. Tack the top of the bag to one wooden slat and the bottom of the bag to the other. Pull all kinds of nesting materials through the holes in the mesh. Add two loops for hanging. Hang the rack outdoors in a place where you can watch the birds when they come shopping for their nesting materials.

RAINBOW BOOK ENDS

WHAT YOU NEED: 2 identical wide-mouthed bottles or jars...salt...food coloring...nail polish...water...bowl...tablespoon

WHAT YOU DO: Put three tablespoons of salt in a bowl. Add a few drops of water at a time until the salt is damp, but not soupy. Add a few drops of coloring to the dampened salt and mix with a spoon until the salt is colored. Pack the colored salt into the bottom of the bottles. Make another salt-and-water mixture the same way, but this time use a different food coloring. Pack this mixture into the bottles on top of the first mixture. Mix salt with a different color for each layer until the bottles are filled. Place the covers on the bottles and paint them with nail polish.

Play with Needle and Thread

SEWING-CARD WALL PICTURES

WHAT YOU NEED: Heavy paper or thin cardboard
... magazine picture ... paints or crayons ...
darning needle ... yarn ... nail ... pins ...
scissors

WHAT YOU DO: Use a magazine picture that has a large simple outline. Pin the picture at the four corners to the paper background. With a nail, punch evenly-spaced holes around the outline of the picture and through the paper background beneath. Remove the pins and the magazine picture. Thread the needle with yarn and sew in and out of the holes of the outline. If you want a solid outline, sew around the picture in the other direction, so that you cover the spaces that were left between the stitches the first time. Color and decorate the picture. Make two holes at the top and pull a piece of yarn through the holes for hanging.

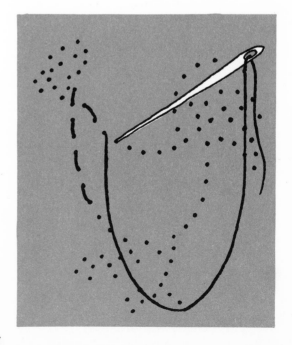

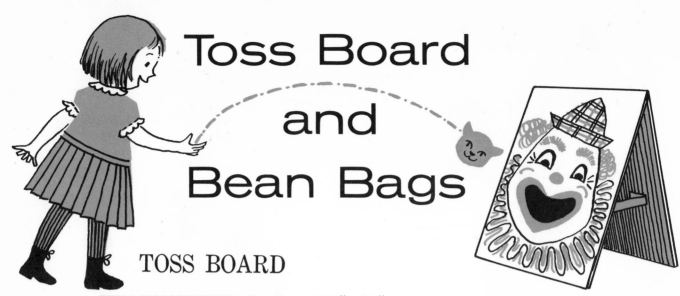

Toss Board and Bean Bags

TOSS BOARD

WHAT YOU NEED: Cardboard 12″ x 24″ . . . crayons . . . gummed tape . . . scissors . . . bean bag

WHAT YOU DO: Fold the cardboard in half so that it measures 12″ x 12″. Draw a clown's head with a very wide open mouth on the front. The mouth must be larger than the bean bag you are going to use. Have an older person cut out the mouth opening. Color the clown's head. Place a small piece of gummed tape inside the folded cardboard, attaching one end to the front, and the other end to the back. This will brace the toss board. To play Bean Bag Toss, stand some distance away and try to toss the bag into the clown's mouth.

BEAN BAGS

WHAT YOU NEED: Cloth (the size of a paper napkin will make two bean bags) . . . dried beans, peas, or small buttons or nuts . . . strong thread . . . needle . . . pencil . . . crayons . . . scissors . . . pins

WHAT YOU DO: Fold the cloth in half so that you have two thicknesses. Pin the edges together so they won't come apart. Draw an animal's head on the cloth with pencil. Draw in the features. Cut the head out. Pin the front and the back together. Thread the needle and sew small tight overcast stitches all around the head, leaving an opening at the top for filling. Half fill the bag with beans and sew up the top opening.

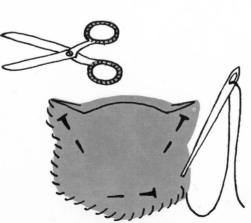

Play with Shells

Most boys and girls like to collect sea shells, from which many lovely things can be made. Before you start to work with shells have some older person clean them in laundry bleach and rinse and dry them thoroughly.

LAPEL PIN

WHAT YOU NEED: Shell . . . ribbon . . . pink nail polish . . . safety pin . . . awl or drill

WHAT YOU DO: Have an older person make a hole in the shell with an awl or drill. Pull a piece of ribbon through the hole. Paint the shell with nail polish. When dry attach a safety pink to the ribbon.

NECKLACE

WHAT YOU NEED: Small thin shells . . . gold or silver paint . . . yarn . . . heavy darning needle

WHAT YOU DO: Paint the shells silver or gold and allow them to dry thoroughly. Thread the darning needle with yarn. String the shells together by piercing them through the center with the needle.

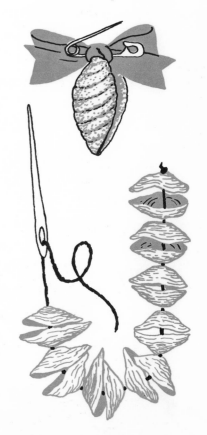

ASHTRAY

WHAT YOU NEED: Large clam shell . . . small shells . . . glue . . . colorless nail polish . . . pearls . . . sequins

WHAT YOU DO: Paint half a clam shell with colorless nail polish and allow it to dry. Glue small shells, pearls and sequins along the wider back edge of the shell.

Play with Sound and Music

Music is fun...because we can sing, dance and play to it. Music is a language everybody understands. Make your own music!

TAMBOURINE

WHAT YOU NEED: 2 paper plates ... stapler ... nail ... string ... jingle bells ... crayons

WHAT YOU DO: Have an older person staple (or sew) two paper plates together facing each other. Make holes around the plates and tie jingle bells to the holes with string. Decorate the tambourine with crayons. Shake to play.

DRUM

WHAT YOU NEED: Empty oatmeal box with cover ... string ... nail ... 2 pencils ...2 spools

WHAT YOU DO: Place the cover on the box. Use the nail to make a hole in the center of the cover and in the center of the bottom of the box. Through these holes, pull a piece of string long enough to hang around your neck and down to your waist. For drumsticks place the spools at the ends of the pencils. Beat to play.

CHIMES

WHAT YOU NEED: Ruler ... large nails ... string ... mixing spoon

WHAT YOU DO: Hang the nails from the ruler with pieces of string. Strike the nails with the mixing spoon to play.

HORN

WHAT YOU NEED: Paper towel roll . . . waxed paper ... rubber band ... nail

WHAT YOU DO: Cover one end of the towel roll with waxed paper and hold it in place with a rubber band. Punch a row of holes along one side of the roll with a nail. Sing a tune into the open end of the horn.

CYMBALS

WHAT YOU NEED: 2 matching pot covers...yarn or ribbon

WHAT YOU DO: Tie ribbon or yarn around the handles of the pot covers. Strike together to play.

XYLOPHONES

WHAT YOU NEED: Tall glasses or quart milk bottles...water...mixing spoon

WHAT YOU DO: Fill the glasses with different amounts of water. The more water in the glass the lower the pitch; less water will raise the pitch. Strike the glasses with the mixing spoon to play.

COMB BUZZER

WHAT YOU NEED: Pocket comb . . . tissue paper

WHAT YOU DO: Fold a piece of tissue paper over the tooth edge of the comb. Hum through the paper to play.

GUITAR

WHAT YOU NEED: Empty cigar or shoe box...rubber bands

WHAT YOU DO: Remove the cover from the box. Stretch rubber bands around the box. Pluck or strum to play.

HAND BELLS

WHAT YOU NEED: Wooden package carrier...4 jingle bells...string

WHAT YOU DO: Tie two jingle bells to each side of the package carrier. Shake to play.

Play with Plants

SPICE ORANGE SACHET BALL

WHAT YOU NEED: Orange . . . whole cloves . . . ribbon . . . pins

WHAT YOU DO: Press cloves all around the orange. Pin a ribbon bow to the top of the orange. This ball will absorb odors and remain fresh a long time.

PORCUPINE POTATO PLANTER

WHAT YOU NEED: Potato . . . 2 colored thumbtacks . . . 4 golf tees . . . soil . . . grass or bird seed . . . pipe cleaner . . . spoon . . . scissors

WHAT YOU DO: Select a potato with a pointed end. Scoop out the top of the potato, leaving a shell about a half an inch thick. Press thumbtacks into the pointed end for eyes. Press a small twist of pipe cleaner into the rear end for a tail. Fill the opening in the planter with soil and sprinkle seeds over the top. Water regularly and the porcupine should have "bristles" in about ten days.

A CARROT GARDEN

WHAT YOU NEED: Carrots ... shallow bowl ... pebbles, stones or colored fish bowl chips (buy them in pet stores) ... water ... knife

WHAT YOU DO: Cut off about two inches of each carrot from the leaf end. Cut off the wilted leaves. Place the cut off pieces in a shallow bowl with the cut ends down. Place pebbles around the carrots to hold them in place. Fill the bowl half full of water. In a few days graceful, feathery leaves will start to grow out of the top. Keep the pebbles moist all the time.

AND WINDOWSILL GARDENS

WHAT YOU NEED: Lemonade or baby food cans ... flower seeds (petunia, nasturtium, etc.) ... soil ... paint

WHAT YOU DO: Have an older person remove the top of the cans with a safety-type opener. Then wash out the cans thoroughly. When dry, paint the cans. When the paint is dry fill the cans half full of soil and plant flower seeds in the soil. Keep the plants watered and in about ten days you will have plant seedlings that can be transplanted outdoors in the spring.

Play with Pencil, Paper and Pennies

PENNY PICTURES

WHAT YOU NEED: Pennies (or larger coins) . . . paper . . . pencil

WHAT YOU DO: On a piece of paper, draw around the coin with a pencil. Add as many pencil details as you like. After you have made as many Penny Pictures as you want, try making pictures using a square, triangle, or any other geometric form in place of the penny. You can combine several forms, if you like.

64

WATER COLOR

CRAYON

PASTE

1